CONTEN

Pedigree

Published 2011. Pedigree Books Ltd, Beech Hill House, Walnut Gardens, Exeter, Devon EX4 4DH
books@pedigreegroup.co.uk www.pedigreebooks.com

£6.99

Qui-Gon Jinn

PROFILE

A wise Jedi knight with a roguish personality, Qui-Gon is never afraid to speak his mind. His faith in the Jedi Order matches his strength in the Force.

"Your focus determines your reality."

Darth Maul

PROFILE

Darth Maul has been training in the ways of the Sith for many years, preparing for the moment when he can strike his enemies down. He is ruthless and deadly.

"At last we will have revenge."

Padmé Amidala

PROFILE

Intelligent, honest and loyal, Padmé is a true believer in the power of democracy. She has strong political ideals and is passionate about justice.

"To live in fear is no life at all."

Jar Jar Binks

PROFILE

Clumsy Jar Jar Binks is a true-hearted Gungan whose capacity for friendship and loyalty is as great as his penchant for making mistakes.

"How wude!"

Star Wars Alphabet

This picture alphabet is unfinished. In some places, the picture is missing. In other places, the word is missing. Can you help?

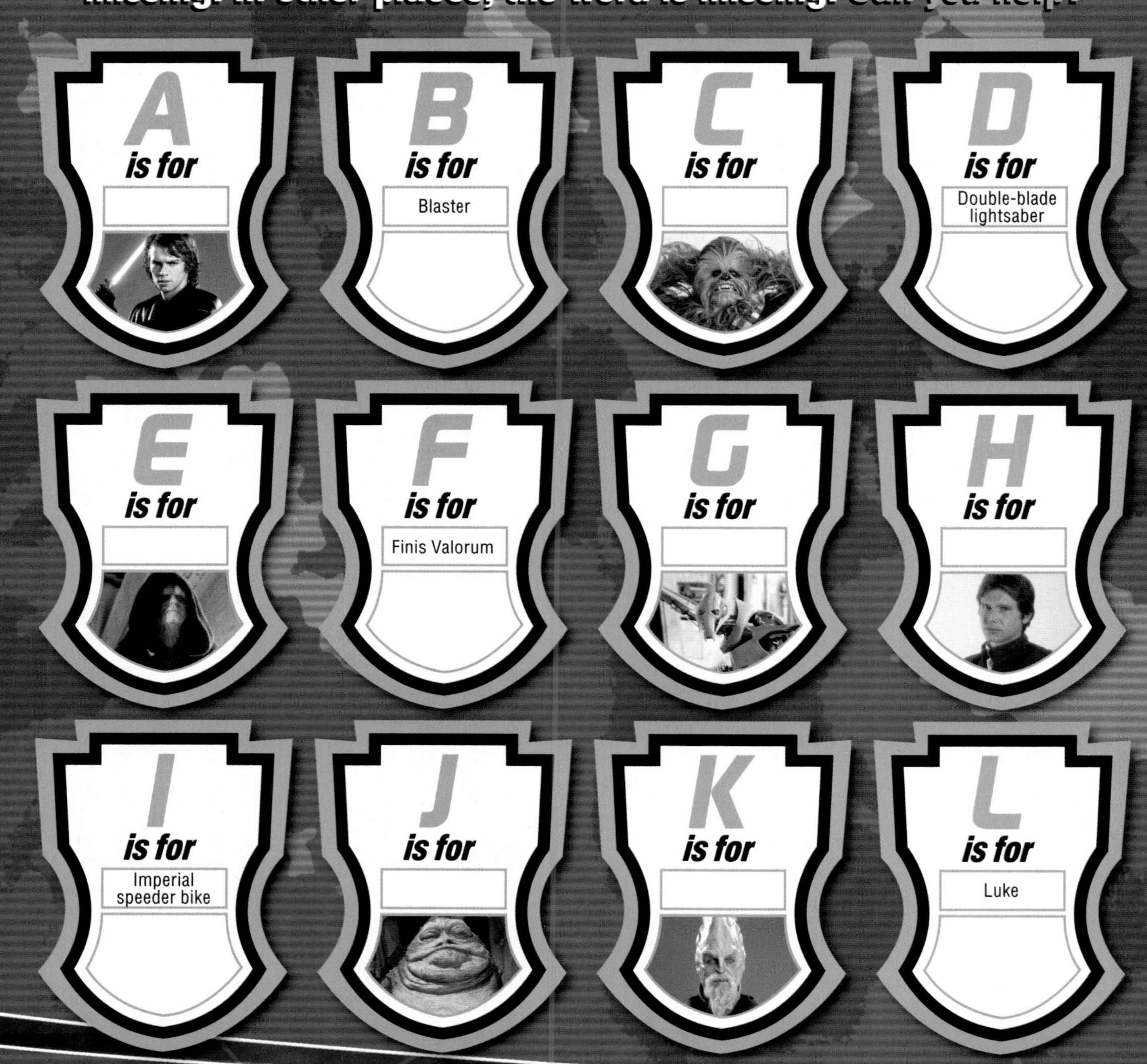

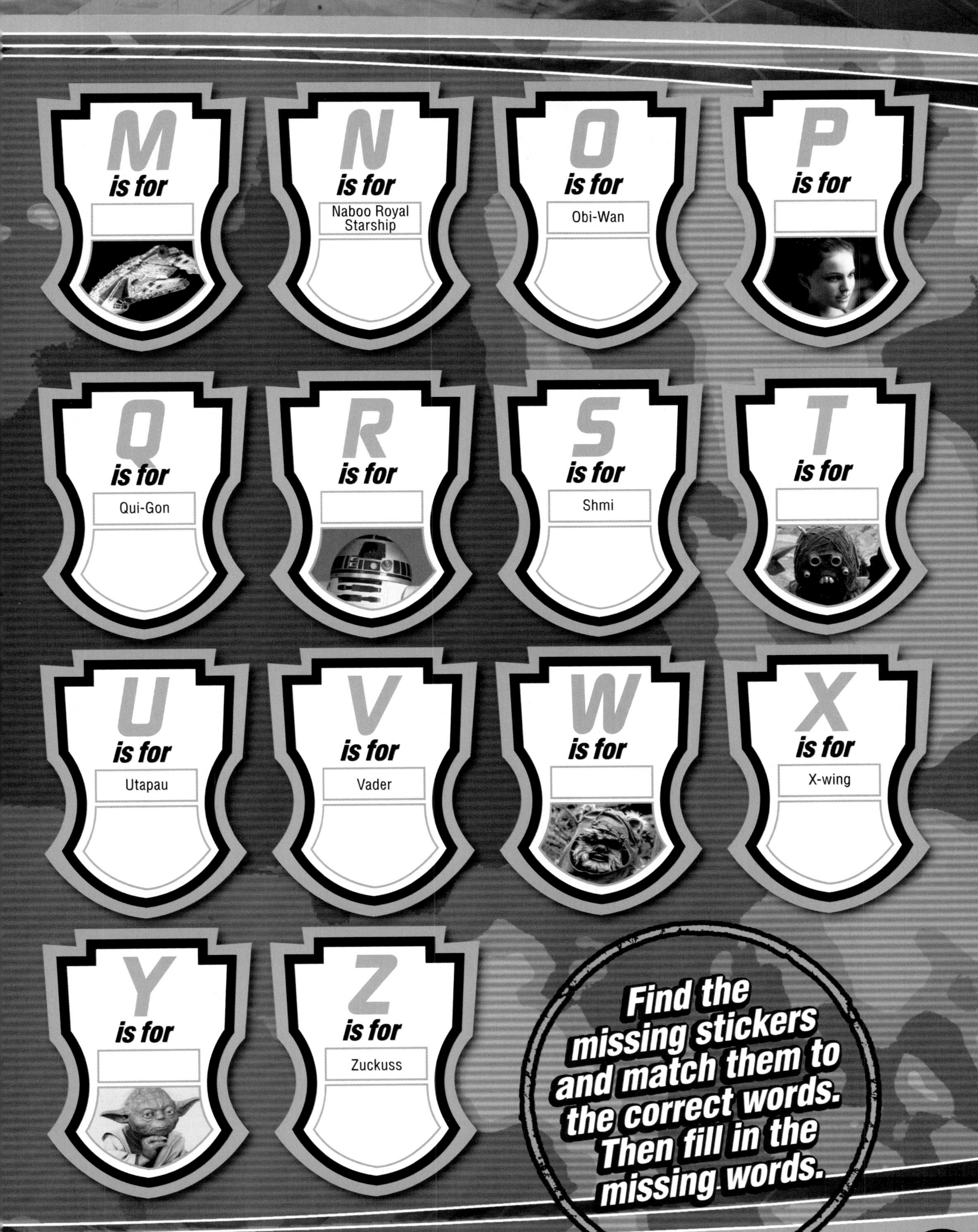

Find the missing stickers and match them to the correct words. Then fill in the missing words.

oot the Differenc

k carefully at these photos of Jar Jar Binks and Qui-Gon Jinn. They look the s
but there are ten small differences. Can you find them all?

Wordsearch

Do you have the sharp eyes of a Jedi? There are fifteen names hidden in this grid. Look carefully and try to find them all.

T	I	N	F	X	E	D	A	K	C	O	L	B	O	R
B	U	M	G	L	C	W	A	R	L	T	E	W	D	B
O	A	C	D	T	I	N	E	T	A	N	E	S	T	Q
B	D	O	E	I	T	N	J	B	S	X	M	D	A	W
I	C	R	A	E	N	E	E	T	Y	O	S	I	T	H
S	N	U	H	R	E	Y	D	G	A	P	L	O	O	A
A	I	S	T	A	R	F	I	G	H	T	E	R	O	H
T	E	C	W	S	P	Z	V	U	Q	T	O	D	I	K
R	N	A	A	N	P	C	E	N	V	C	T	I	N	L
H	T	N	D	N	A	L	M	G	A	O	S	A	E	G
N	R	T	O	W	T	K	J	A	O	G	C	R	O	I
X	F	W	I	T	W	M	D	N	G	N	E	E	U	Q
E	O	A	A	O	R	E	A	C	T	O	L	E	I	H
T	S	B	M	N	H	S	I	N	A	B	O	O	O	S
D	G	N	I	C	A	R	D	O	P	U	H	C	N	U

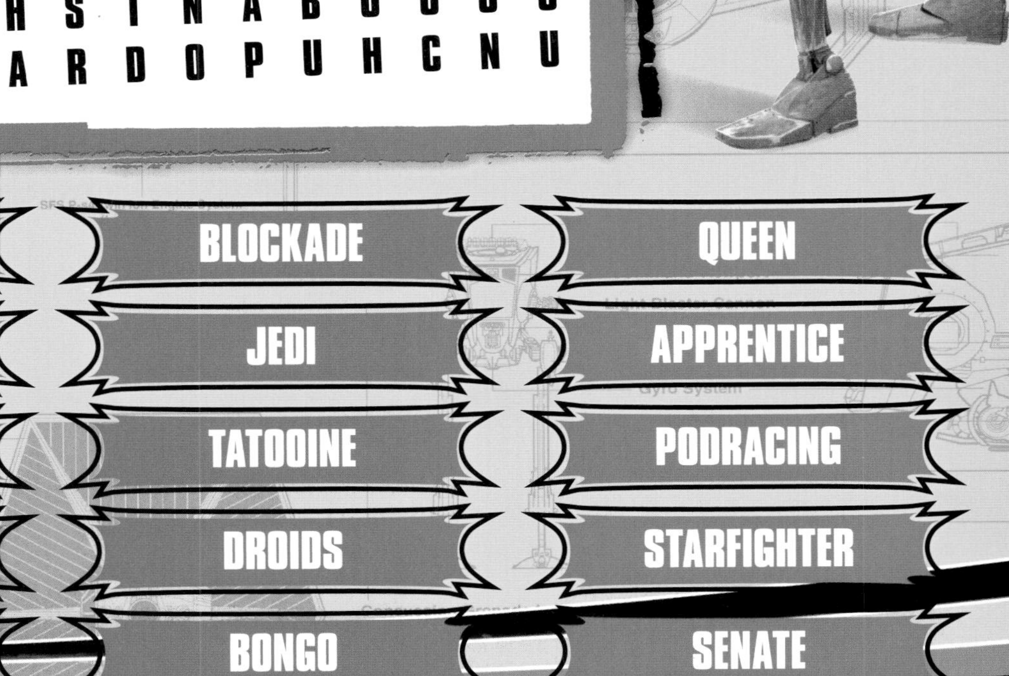

NABOO
BLOCKADE
QUEEN
CORUSCANT
JEDI
APPRENTICE
SITH
TATOOINE
PODRACING
GUNGAN
DROIDS
STARFIGHTER
BATTLE
BONGO
SENATE

Portrait Painter

Boss Nass wants his portrait painted! Use the grid below to draw the Gungan leader. Then colour in your picture.

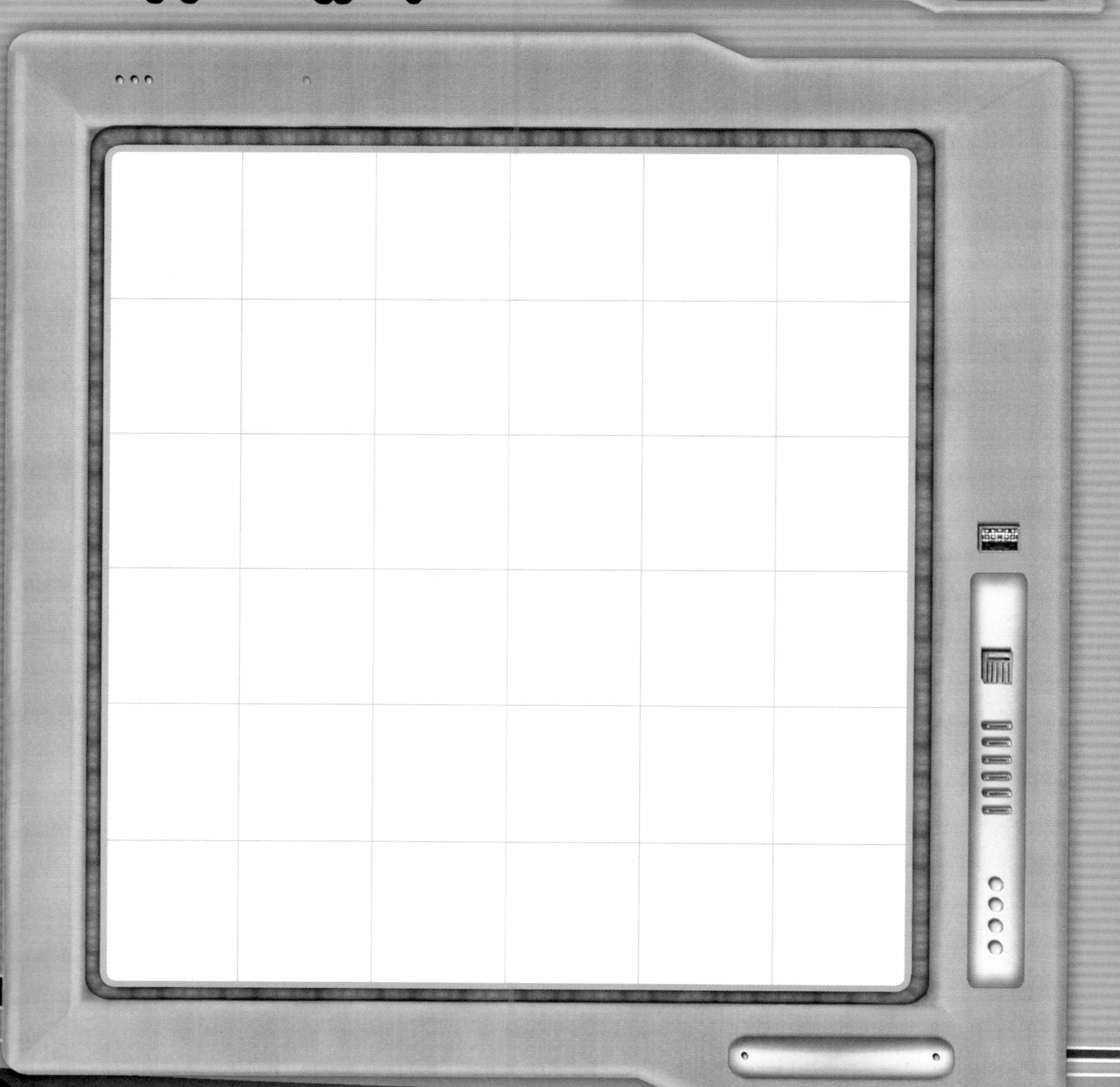

TRUE OR FALSE?

Look at these historical statements. **Can you pick out the truths from the falsehoods?**

5 Darth Maul first fought Qui-Gon Jinn on Tatooine.

6 Supreme Chancellor Valorum was the Senator for Naboo.

1 Padmé Amidala married Bail Organa.

7 Darth Maul was a secretly trained Jedi Knight.

2 Obi-Wan Kenobi was a Padawan when he met Anakin Skywalker.

8 The Trade Federation blockaded Naboo.

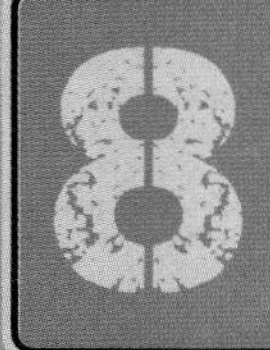

3 The Battle of Naboo was the first battle of the Clone Wars.

9 Shmi Skywalker was married to a farmer called Watto.

4 Anakin Skywalker was a slave boy who belonged to Jabba the Hutt.

10 Anakin Skywalker built C-3PO.

Star Wars Quiz Part 1

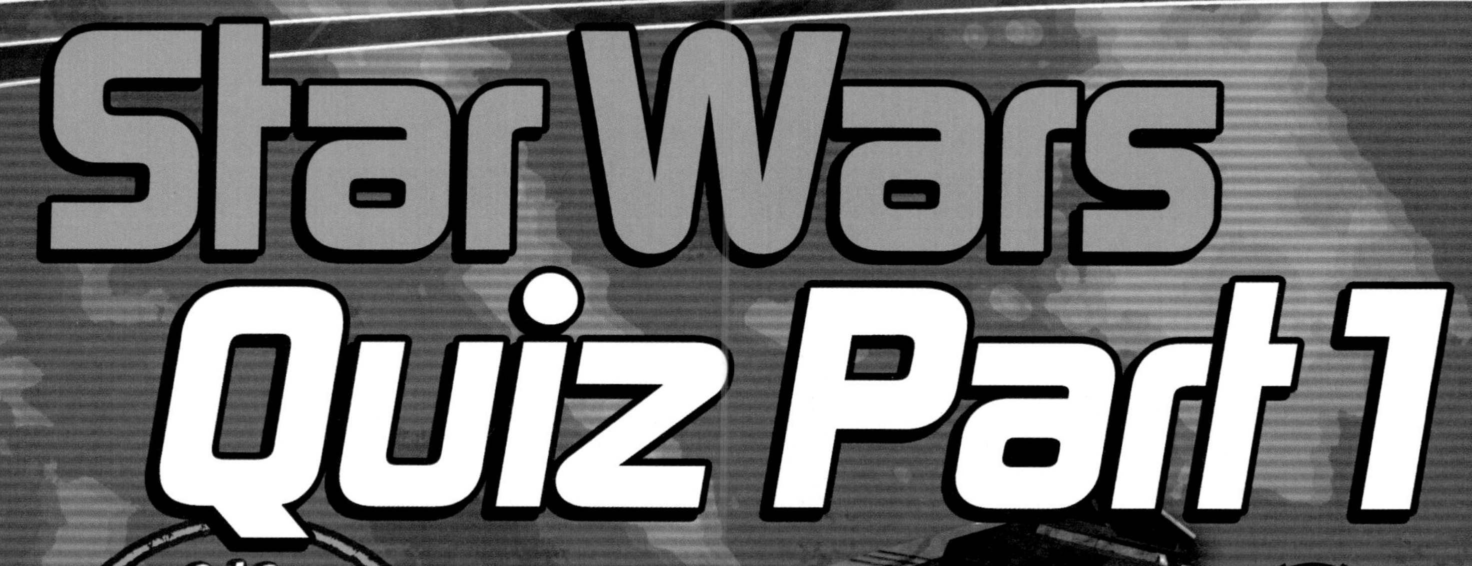

Set a timer for one minute, and try to name each person, technology or vehicle in these pictures in under sixty seconds.

1

2

3

4

5

6
7
8
9
10
Check your answers and enter your score here:

Obi-Wan Kenobi

PROFILE

Obi-Wan Kenobi is a thoughtful, compassionate and witty Jedi, who has great faith in the Force. His strength of character and steady patience are often needed when dealing with his Padawan, Anakin Skywalker.

"Use the Force."

Count Dooku

PROFILE

Count Dooku was once a Jedi, but he has turned away from the Order to pursue his personal ambitions. He is greedy and cruel, but he is also a masterful warrior and strong in the Force.

"I've become more powerful than any Jedi."

Palpatine

PROFILE

The Supreme Chancellor rose to his position over a number of years. He listens carefully to his Jedi advisors, and his quiet character conceals a determined personality.

"I love democracy."

Jango Fett

PROFILE

The original of the Republic's clone army is willing to sell his services to the highest bidder. The one person he truly cares about is his son, Boba.

"I'm just a simple man, trying to make my way in the universe."

STICKER

Use your stickers to complete this picture

JIGSAW

of the famous Battle of Geonosis.

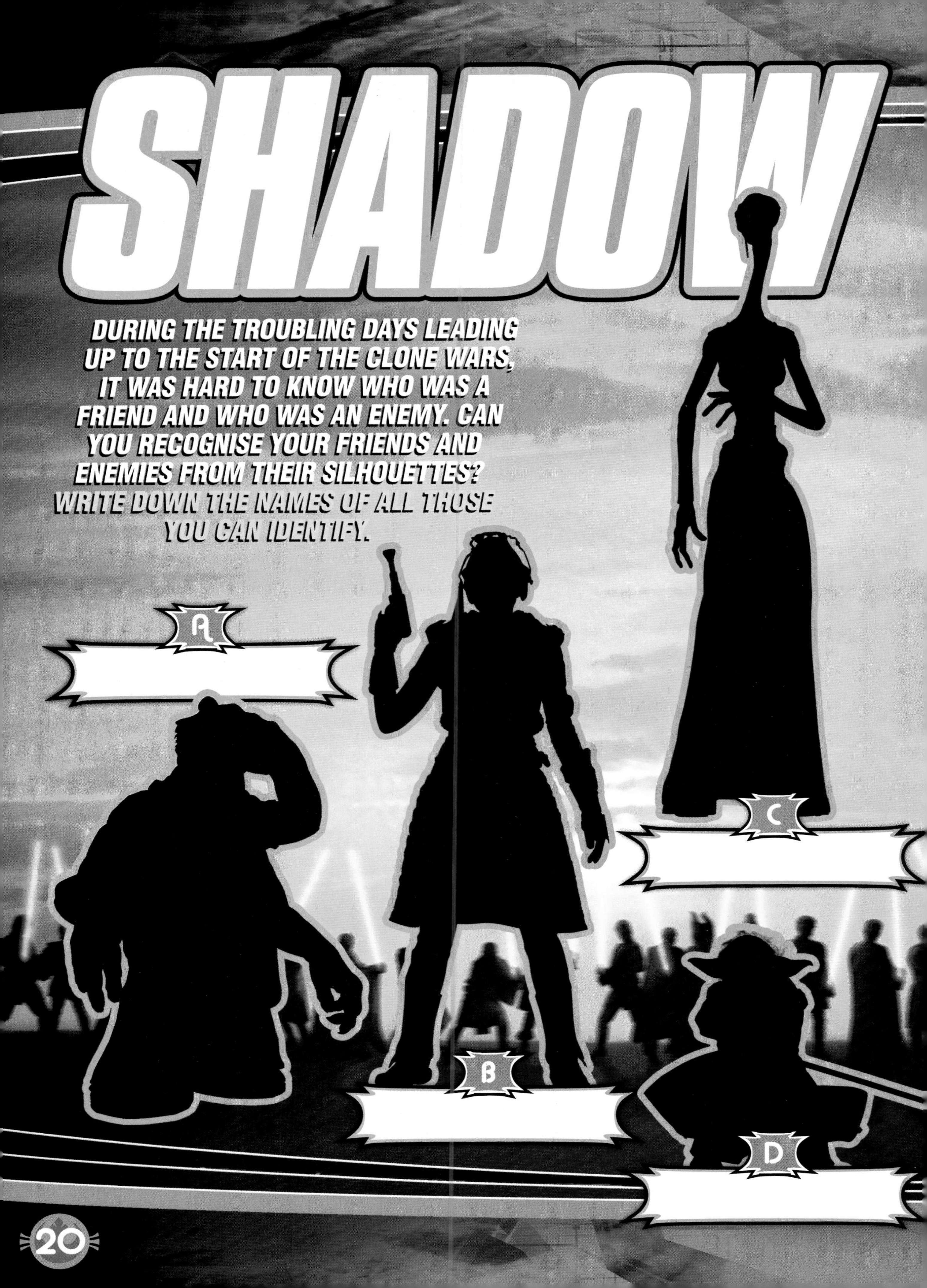
SHADOW
DURING THE TROUBLING DAYS LEADING UP TO THE START OF THE CLONE WARS, IT WAS HARD TO KNOW WHO WAS A FRIEND AND WHO WAS AN ENEMY. CAN YOU RECOGNISE YOUR FRIENDS AND ENEMIES FROM THEIR SILHOUETTES? WRITE DOWN THE NAMES OF ALL THOSE YOU CAN IDENTIFY.
A
B
C
D

SPOTTER
E
F
G
H

WHO AM I?

Read the lines below and decide who each of them is describing.

1 I have green skin and am short in comparison to my fellow Jedi.
My name is:

2 I am bald and I carry a purple lightsaber.
My name is:

3
I am tall with grey hair and a grey beard. I wear a dark cloak and can use Force lightning.
My name is:
4
I have a large belly and four arms – good for serving customers!
My name is:
5
I have green, mottled skin and red eyes. I am never seen without my ceremonial black hat.
My name is:
6
I wear the armour that I got when I fought alongside the Mandalorians. I can fly using the jetpack on my back.
My name is:

Star Wars Quiz Part2

Galactic history has been recorded in six episodes:

A

THE PHANTOM MENACE

B

ATTACK OF THE CLONES

C

REVENGE OF THE SITH

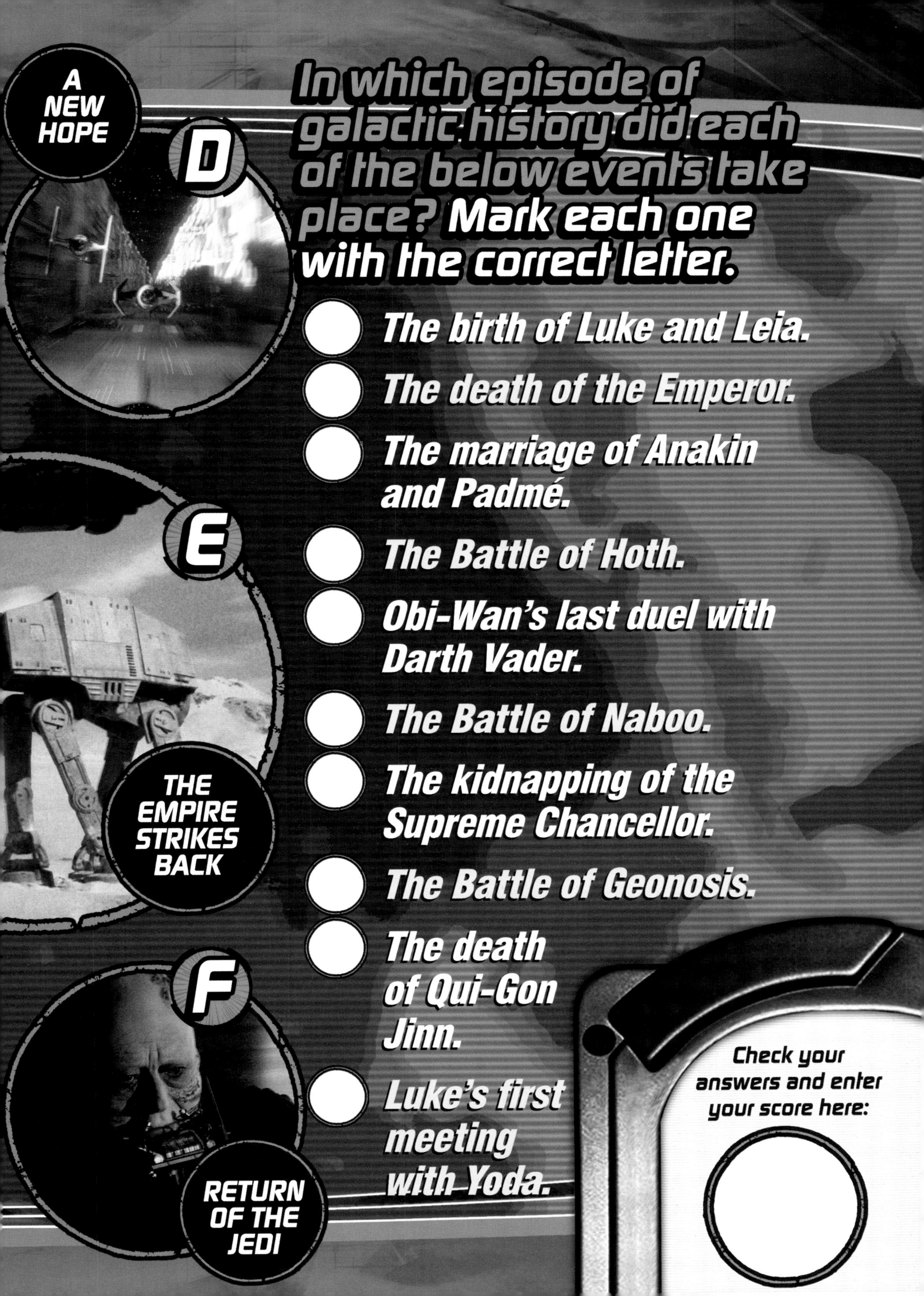
A NEW HOPE
D
In which episode of galactic history did each of the below events take place? Mark each one with the correct letter.
The birth of Luke and Leia.
The death of the Emperor.
The marriage of Anakin and Padmé.
E
The Battle of Hoth.
Obi-Wan's last duel with Darth Vader.
The Battle of Naboo.
THE EMPIRE STRIKES BACK
The kidnapping of the Supreme Chancellor.
The Battle of Geonosis.
F
The death of Qui-Gon Jinn.
Luke's first meeting with Yoda.
RETURN OF THE JEDI
Check your answers and enter your score here:

General Grievous

PROFILE

The fearsome droid general is trained in lightsaber combat and is a ruthless warrior. He collects the lightsabers of fallen Jedi as trophies, and relishes the horror of battle and war.

"Jedi scum!"

Mace Windu

PROFILE

Mace Windu is one of the most respected Jedi Masters on the Council. He has a mischievous sense of humour alongside great wisdom and impressive fighting skills.

"The oppression of the Sith will never return."

Darth Sidious

PROFILE

The evil Sith Lord hides in the shadows, pulling the strings of politicians and leaders like a puppet master. He has been plotting the downfall of the Jedi Order for many years.

"The Sith will rule the galaxy."

Anakin Skywalker

PROFILE

Brave, loving and impulsive, Anakin is one of the brightest stars of the Jedi Order. However, as he grows older and gains more responsibility, the gulf between his heart and his duty is widening.

"I'm not the Jedi I should be."

Star Wars Scene

Create your own galactic scene using your stickers and this deserted planet background. Be as imaginative as you can, and then add your own drawings of characters and droids. When you have completed the scene, describe what is happening in the text box.

In the picture...

ODD ONE OUT

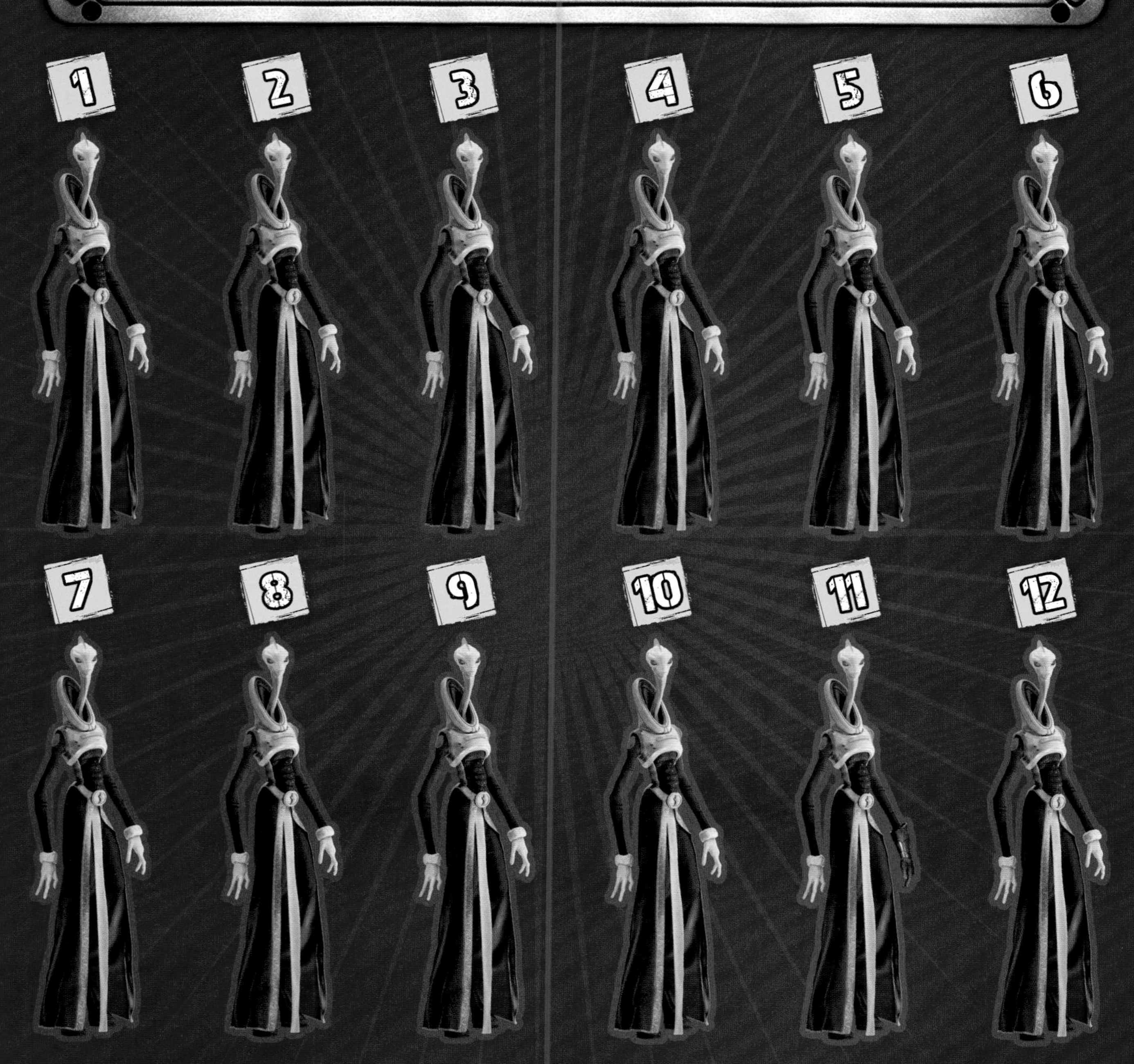

Shapeshifter Zam Wesell has been trying to disguise herself as a Kaminoan, but she hasn't got it quite right. Can you spot the odd one out and identify the assassin?

Wordmaker

How many brand-new words can you make from the name of Dexter Jettster's diner?

DEXTER'S DINER

Colour By Numbers

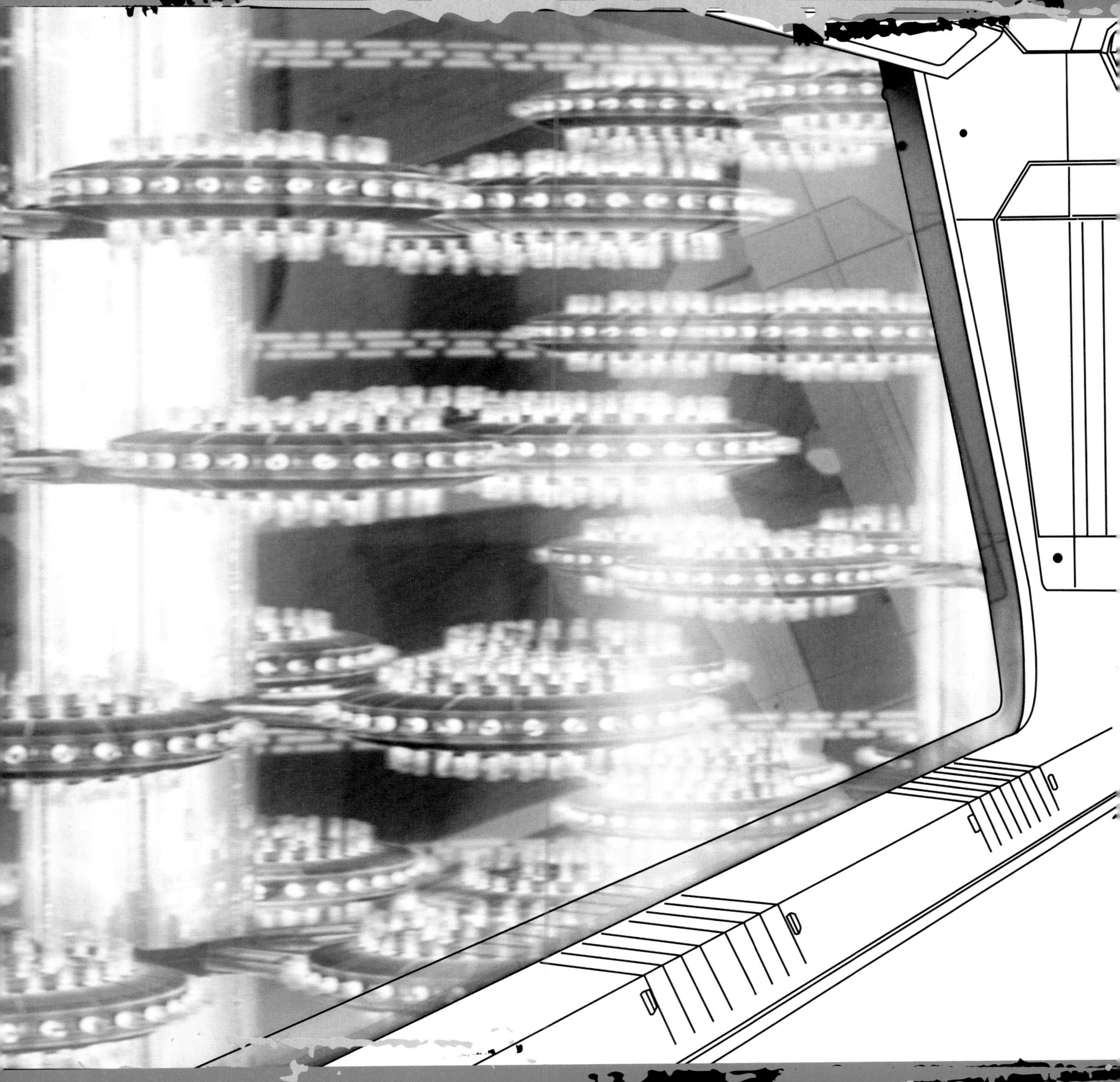

1 2 3 4

When Obi-Wan Kenobi arrived on Kamino, he was shocked to discover that a clone army had been created for the Republic. Use the colour code to complete this picture of his historic meeting with Lama Su.

Star Wars Quiz Part 3

Answer these questions correctly to show how much you know about galactic history.

1 Which Jedi generals rescued the Supreme Chancellor after he was kidnapped?

2 What were Anakin's nightmares about?

3 Where did Obi-Wan find General Grievous after the failed kidnapping plot?

4 Who issued Order 66?

?

5 Where was Yoda when the clones turned on the Jedi?

6
Who killed Mace Windu?
7
How did Obi-Wan Kenobi reach Mustafar?
8
What was Anakin's new name?
9
Who took Padmé's daughter to keep her safe?
?
10
How did Luke Skywalker arrive on Tatooine?
Check your answers and enter your score here:

Galactic
War!

Jedi
heroes

Luke Skywalker

PROFILE

Luke remembers nothing about his parents, but he has inherited their spirit of adventure. He dreams of leaving the barren deserts of Tatooine and exploring the wide galaxy.

"I want to learn the ways of the Force and become a Jedi like my father."

Princess Leia

PROFILE

Padmé's daughter inherited all her political ability and quick-witted diplomacy. Despite her youth, she has already taken her place in the Senate and is ready to stand up for her beliefs.

"Help me, Obi-Wan Kenobi; you're my only hope."

C-3PO

PROFILE

Protocol droid C-3PO began his life on Tatooine, built by Anakin Skywalker when he was a little boy. C-3PO is always worrying and complaining but has shown unfailing loyalty and support to his owners.

"We're doomed."

R2-D2

PROFILE

There can be few astromech droids who are as resourceful or who have witnessed so many important events, as R2-D2. R2-D2 has a special link with the Skywalker family and goes to great lengths to help and protect them.

Complete

1	2	3	3	2	1			
1	5	9	13	17	21			
1	3	1	1	3	1			
1	1	2	0	2	1			
5	1	10	2	15	3			
2	8	10	7	9	16			
15	30	60	120	240	480			
3	9	27	81	243	729			

the Code

The Rebel Alliance uses coded strips of numbers to send news and instructions. R2-D2 has received a new set of codes, but a malfunctioning circuit has deleted the last three sections of each code. Can you use logic to work out how each strip must end?

(Clue: You may need to use a calculator!)

FOLLOW THE TRAIL

A

START

R2-D2 has gone searching for Obi-Wan Kenobi in the Tatooine desert.
Luke and C-3PO are following him, but which trail should they follow?
Trace the line with your finger to discover which way R2-D2 went.
B
FINISH
D
C
E

Writing in Code

Those who help the Rebel Alliance must learn to write all their messages in code, for it is not safe to trust anyone. Start your training by writing your name in code. The key below links every letter of the alphabet with a number. Write your name in numbers in the space provided.

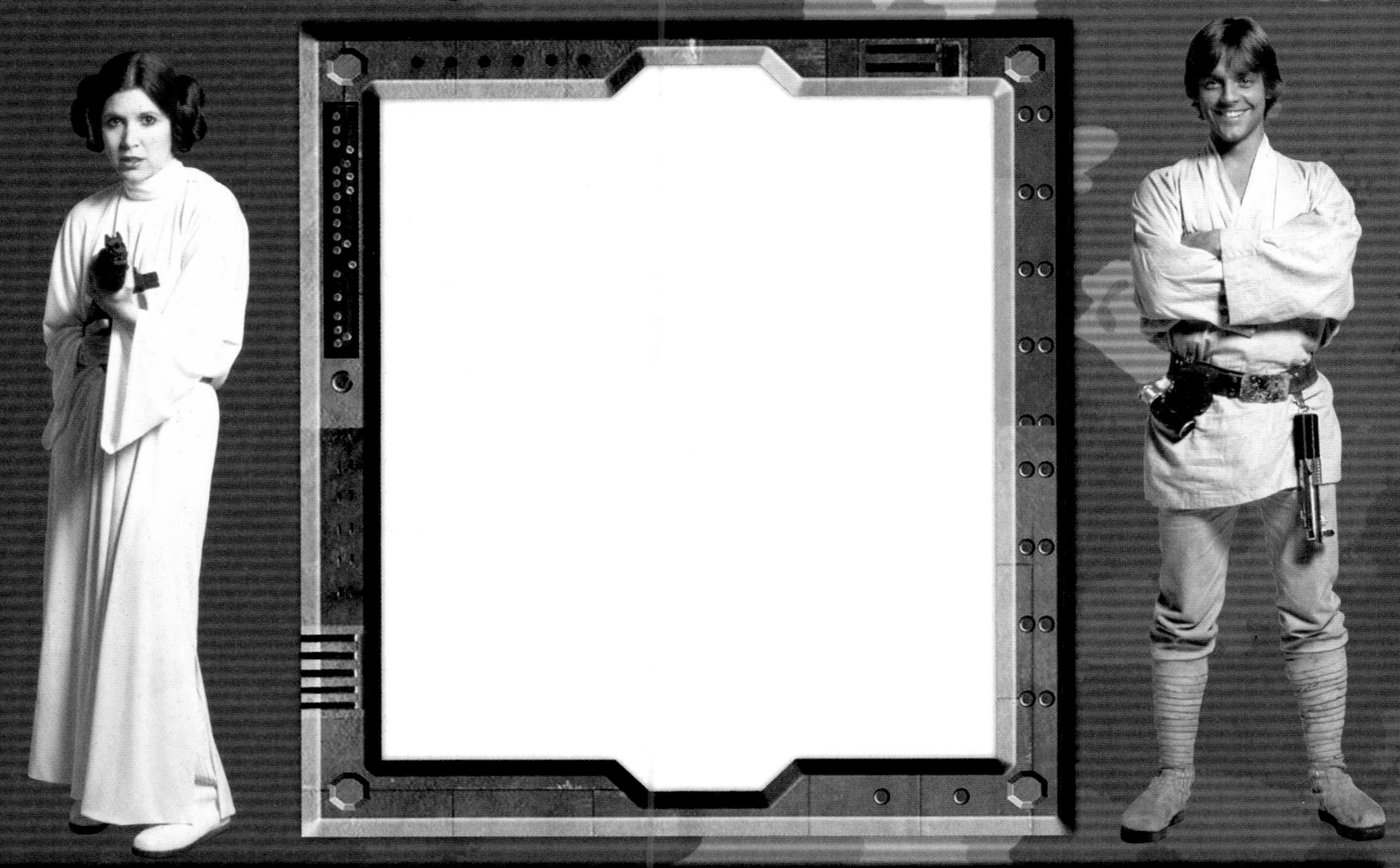

When you have mastered the technique, write a coded letter to your best friend.

A	B	C	D	E	F	G	H	I	J	K	L	M
25	5	9	30	28	4	24	42	6	45	23	1	10

N	O	P	Q	R	S	T	U	V	W	X	Y	Z
7	26	21	44	29	46	2	43	41	8	27	3	22

WHAT AM I?

This mysterious puzzle hides a picture of a particular species. Join the dots in the correct order to find and name the species.

Star Wars Quiz Part 4

Set a timer for two minutes, and try to name what you see before tne timer sounds.

1

2

3

5
6
7
4
8
10
9
Check your answers and enter your score here:

Han Solo

PROFILE

Han Solo has the heart of a pirate and loves the freedom of roaming the galaxy. He is confident, brave and impulsive, and his sarcastic manner hides a loyal friend and a staunch companion.

"Hokey religions and ancient weapons are no match for a good blaster at your side."

Chewbacca

PROFILE

This brave Wookiee was present when the Galactic Republic fell, and he has suffered at the hands of the Empire since those days. He is ready and willing to fight for his beliefs and his friends.

Jabba the Hutt

PROFILE

Crime lord Jabba the Hutt is a grotesque creature, motivated only by greed and revenge. His palace is a place of horror and cruelty.

Yoda

PROFILE

Wise Master Yoda is the oldest and most experienced Jedi on the Council. His kindness, warm humour and strength in the Force have earned him the respect of Jedi and Senators alike.

"My ally is the force, and a powerful ally it is."

Colour Challenge
Some of your favourite heroes need some colour! Use your colouring pens to bring this picture to life.

MAKE AND DO: DESK CALENDAR

FOLLOW THESE SIMPLE STEPS TO MAKE AN EXCITING GALACTIC CALENDAR FOR YOUR DESK.

INSTRUCTIONS:

1. Fold the card along the dotted lines as shown in the diagram.
2. Put glue on the narrowest white folded section and stick this to the back of the opposite end of the card.
3. Wait for the glue to dry, and then stick the calendar in the centre of the front of the card.
4. Use your stickers to decorate the calendar, creating an exciting galactic scene.

WHAT YOU NEED:

- 1 sheet black A4 card
- Your stickers
- A mini stick-in calendar (you can buy these at craft shops)
- Glue

PLACE
CALENDAR
HERE

< Fold here

< Fold here

STAR WARS

< Fold here

Glue here

HOW TO DRAW DOOKU

STEP 1

Draw pencil lines to mark out the position of Count Dooku's body.

FOLLOW THESE SIMPLE STEPS AND LEARN HOW TO DRAW THE INFAMOUS COUNT DOOKU.

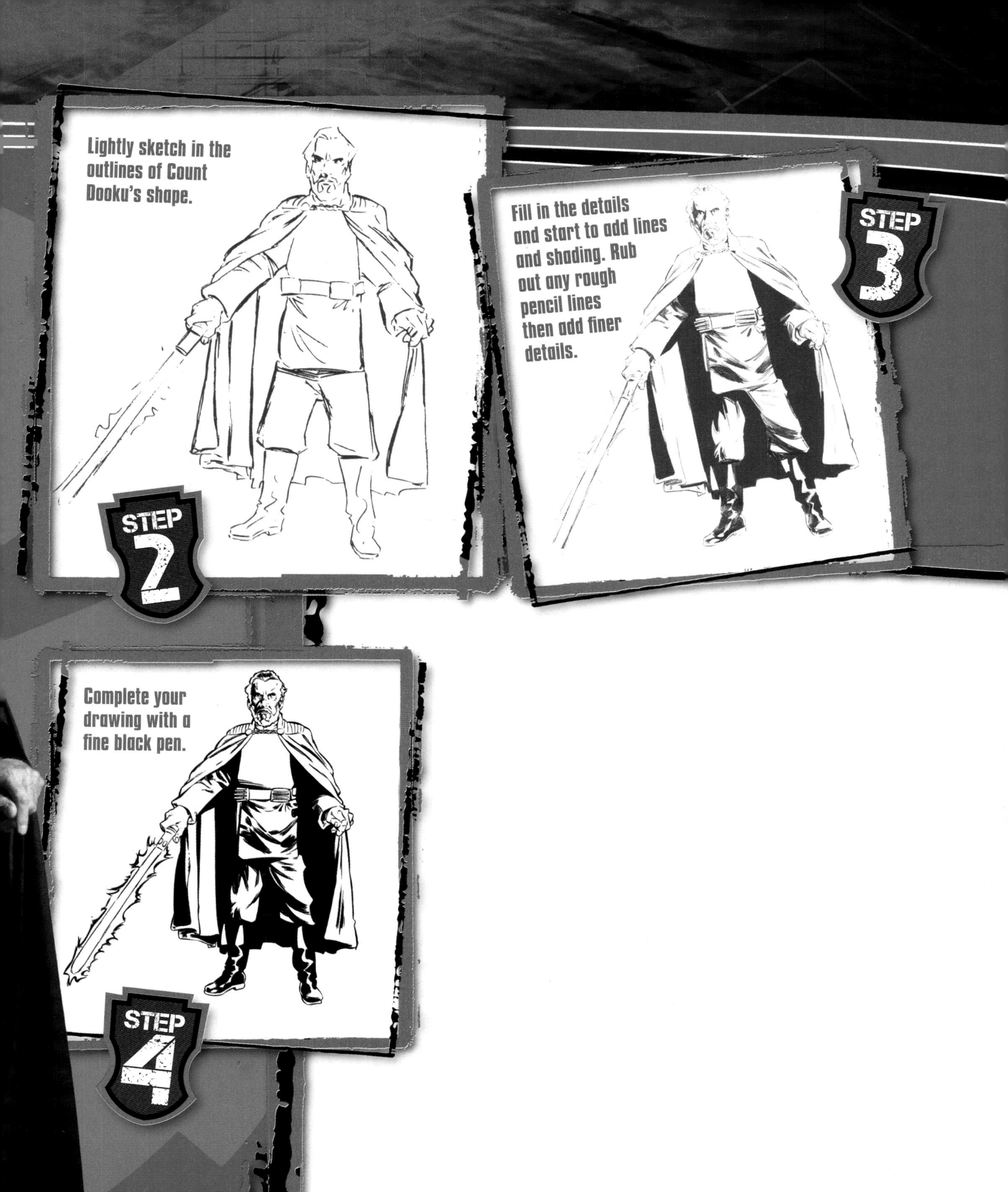
Lightly sketch in the outlines of Count Dooku's shape.
STEP 2
Fill in the details and start to add lines and shading. Rub out any rough pencil lines then add finer details.
STEP 3
Complete your drawing with a fine black pen.
STEP 4

Star Wars Quiz Part 5

Answering these multiple-choice questions correctly requires concentration and focus. Think carefully before you make your choices.

1 What sort of planet is Hoth?
a. Ice
b. Fire
c. Water
Answer:

2 What did Han own that once belonged to Lando Calrissian?
a. A watch
b. A ship
c. A speeder
Answer:

3 Who betrayed Han and his friends to Darth Vader in Cloud City?
a. C-3PO
b. Lando Calrissian
c. Boba Fett
Answer:

4 Where did Luke first meet Yoda?
a. Tatooine
b. Hoth
c. Dagobah
Answer:

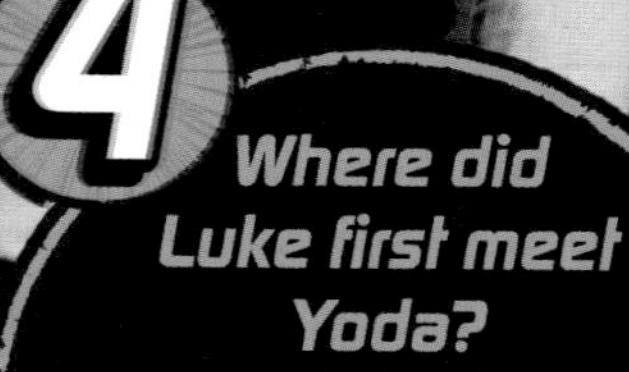

5
Which droid accompanied Luke on his journey to find Yoda?
a. R2-D2
b. C-3PO
c. R2-T7
Answer:

6
What vision did Luke see in a cave during his training?
a. Darth Vader
b. Leia's death
c. Han in danger
Answer:

7
Which monster almost killed Luke on Hoth?
a. Bantha
b. Rancor
c. Wampa
Answer:

8
Who cut off Luke's hand?
a. His sister
b. His father
c. Han Solo
Answer:

9
In what substance was Han Solo frozen?
a. Aconite
b. Carbonite
c. Seranite
Answer:

10
Who claimed the bounty on Han Solo?
a. Zam Wesell
b. Jango Fett
c. Boba Fett
Answer:

Check your answers and enter your score here:

Grand Moff Tarkin

PROFILE

Tarkin has risen high in Imperial ranks, for his love of cruelty appeals to the Emperor. He enjoys inflicting suffering, and has made many enemies.

"The Jedi are extinct."

Boba Fett

PROFILE

Spurred on by a hatred of the Jedi who killed his father, Boba Fett is an enemy of the Rebel Alliance. He is a skilful bounty hunter, and his mysterious armour strikes fear into the hearts of those he hunts.

"He's no good to me dead."

The Emperor

PROFILE

The Emperor was architect of all the pain and suffering that the Clone Wars inflicted. He rules by fear, using his loyal subjects to crush any sign of rebellion with an iron fist. It seems impossible that he can ever be toppled from his position of power.

"Your feeble skills are no match for the power of the dark side."

Darth Vader

PROFILE

The Emperor's loyal apprentice has enforced his laws across the galaxy, and it seems that everything that was good in Anakin Skywalker has died. Darth Vader shows no mercy.

"Don't underestimate the Force."

Answering Back

Princess Leia is quick-witted and always has a retort on the tip of her tongue. But at whom did she aim these insults?

1. Will someone get this big walking carpet out of my way?

Answer:

2. You stuck up, half-witted, scruffy-looking nerf herder!

Answer:

3. I don't know where you get your delusions, laser brain.

Answer:

4. I recognised your foul stench when I was brought on board.

Answer:

5. You came in that thing? You're braver than I thought.

Answer:

6. You're a jittery little thing, aren't you?

Answer:

7. Some day you're gonna be wrong, I just hope I'm there to see it.

Answer:

8. This bucket of bolts is never going to get us past that blockade.

Answer:

9. Aren't you a little short for a stormtrooper?

Answer:

THE NEW ORDER

After defeating the Emperor, a daunting challenge lies ahead. A new Jedi Order is required to maintain peace in the galaxy.

If you were Luke, what decisions would you make about the new Order? Put yourself in his place and design a fresh symbol for the new Jedi Order. Use these templates to fire your imagination.

PLANET PICKER

These Rebels can now return to their home worlds. But which planet does each of them call home? Find the correct stickers and help the rebels to go home.

D
G
F
E
H

WORK PATH

Solve the clues to complete the word path that will lead the heroes across the deep chasm. The last letter of each word is also the first letter of the next word. Good luck!

1. A worrisome protocol droid.
2. The first name of Qui-Gon Jinn's Padawan.
3. Palpatine's home planet.
4. The first name of Luke's uncle on Tatooine.
5. Gunray's first name.

Join the Jedi Order

Stick photo here

What would you look like if you were a Jedi Knight? What sort of lightsaber would you have? What would you wear?

Stick a small photo of your face over the face in the template. Then use your colouring pens and stickers to turn yourself into a Jedi Knight!

Star Wars Quiz Part 6

The final part of the quiz tests your loyalty. Answer simply 'yes' or 'no' to each question.

1 Do you have a best friend?

Yes ● No ●

2 Do you apologise when you are in the wrong?

Yes ● No ●

3 Have you ever faced your biggest fear?

Yes ● No ●

4 Have you ever forgiven someone?

Yes ● No ●

5
Do you believe in the Force?
Yes No

6
Would you like to be a Jedi?
Yes No

7
Do you like meeting new people?
Yes No

8
Can you keep a secret?
Yes No

9
Have you ever felt scared?
Yes No

10
Have you ever stood up for something you believe in?
Yes No

Give yourself one point for every 'yes' answer and enter your score here:

Now add up your scores for all six quizzes and find out your results.

0–34
Your attention has been wandering and your focus has suffered. It is important to relax, but your life needs an equal balance of work and play. Try harder and you will improve your score.

35–49
You have done well, but there is room for improvement before you can move on to begin your training. If you work hard, you can achieve anything.

50–60
You are an exceptional student! The Jedi Order would be glad to accept you and begin your training at once. You have the qualities a true Jedi Knight requires – focus, loyalty, kindness and intelligence.

ANSWERS

PAGES 8-9

A is for **ANAKIN** B is for **BLASTER**
C is for **CHEWBACCA**
D is for **DOUBLE-BLADE LIGHTSABER**
E is for **EMPEROR** F is for **FINIS VALORUM**
G is for **GENERAL GRIEVOUS** H is for **HAN**
I is for **IMPERIAL SPEEDER BIKE**
J is for **JABBA** K is for **KI-ADI-MUNDI**
L is for **LUKE**
M is for ***MILLENNIUM FALCON***
N is for **NABOO ROYAL STARSHIP**
O is for **OBI-WAN** P is for **PADMÉ**
Q is for **QUI-GON** R is for **R2-D2**
S is for **SHMI** T is for **TUSKEN RAIDERS**
U is for **UTAPAU** V is for **VADER**
W is for **WICKET W. WARRICK**
X is for **X-WING** Y is for **YODA**
Z is for **ZUCKUSS**

PAGE 10

PAGE 11

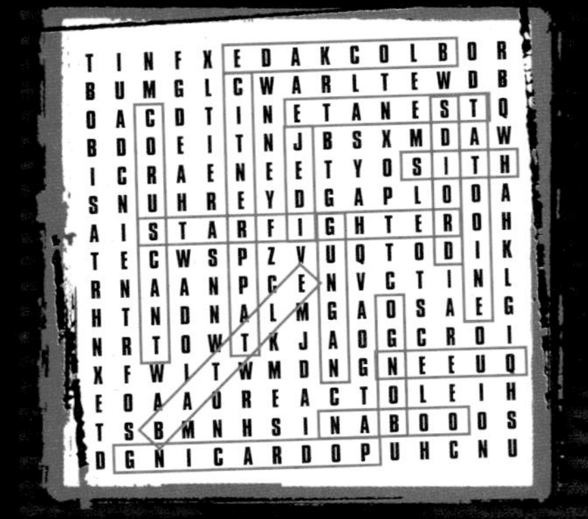

PAGE 13

1. **FALSE.** 2. **TRUE.** 3. **FALSE.**
4. **FALSE.** 5. **TRUE.** 6. **FALSE.**
7. **FALSE.** 8. **TRUE.** 9. **FALSE.** 10. **TRUE.**

PAGES 14-15

1. **Jedi starfighter** 2. **Naboo Royal Cruiser**
3. **Nute Gunray** 4. **A99 aquata breather**
5. **Bantha** 6. **Droideka** 7. **Sebulba** 8. **Jawa**
9. **Sith speeder** 10. **Captain Panaka**

PAGE 20

a. **Dexter Jettster** b. **Zam Wesell**
c. **Lama Su** d. **Master Yoda**
e. **Jango Fett** f. **Count Dooku**
g. **Tusken Raider** h. **Poggle the Lesser**

PAGES 22-23

1. **Yoda** 2. **Mace Windu**
3. **Count Dooku** 4. **Dexter Jettster**
5. **Rune Haako** 6. **Jango Fett**

PAGES 24-25

1. **c** 2. **f** 3. **b** 4. **e** 5. **d** 6. **a**
7. **c** 8. **b** 9. **a** 10. **e**

PAGE 30

11

PAGES 34-35

1. **Anakin Skywalker and Obi-Wan Kenobi**
2. **Padmé's death in childbirth** 3. **Utapau**
4. **Palpatine** 5. **Kashyyyk** 6. **Palpatine**
7. **He stowed away on board Padmé's ship** 8. **Darth Vader** 9. **Bail Organa**
10. **Obi-Wan Kenobi took Luke to his uncle's farm**

PAGES 40-41

1	2	3	3	2	1	1	2	3
1	5	9	13	17	21	25	29	33
1	3	1	1	3	1	1	3	1
1	1	2	0	2	1	1	0	1
5	1	10	2	15	3	20	4	25
2	8	10	7	9	16	12	10	22
15	30	60	120	240	480	960	1920	3840
3	9	27	81	243	729	2187	6561	19683

PAGE 42

B

PAGE 45

Gungan

PAGES 46-47

1. **Stormtrooper** 2. **Greedo**
3. ***Millennium Falcon*** 4. **Death Star**
5. **X-wing starfighter**
6. **Grand Moff Tarkin** 7. **Tusken Raider**
8. **Jabba the Hutt** 9. **TIE fighter**
10. ***Slave I***

PAGES 56-57

1. **a** 2. **b** 3. **b** 4. **c** 5. **a**
6. **a** 7. **c** 8. **b** 9. **b** 10. **c**

PAGE 60

1. **Chewbacca** 2. **Han Solo** 3. **Han Solo**
4. **Grand Hoff Tarkin** 5. **Han Solo and the *Millennium Falcon*** 6. **Wicket W. Warrick**
7. **Han Solo** 8. **The *Millennium Falcon***
9. **Luke Skywalker** 10. **Han Solo**

PAGES 62-63

a. **Kashyyyk** b. **Chandrila**
c. **Mon Calamari** d. **Socorro** e. **Corellia**
f. **Kamino** g. **Endor** h. **Naboo**

PAGE 64

C3POBIWANABOOWENUTE

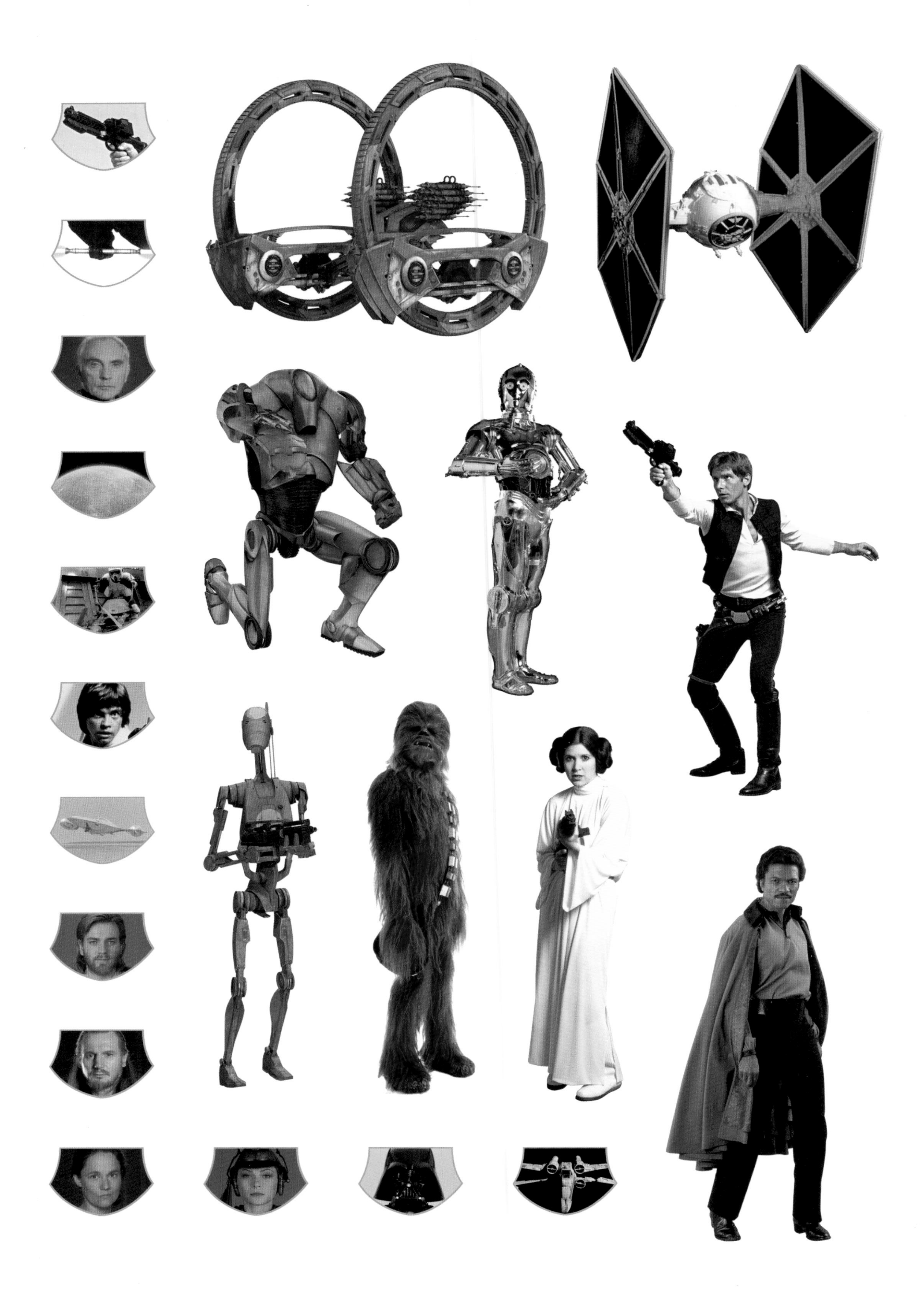

KASHYYYK

CHANDRILA

CALAMARI

SOCORRO

CORELLIA

KAMINO

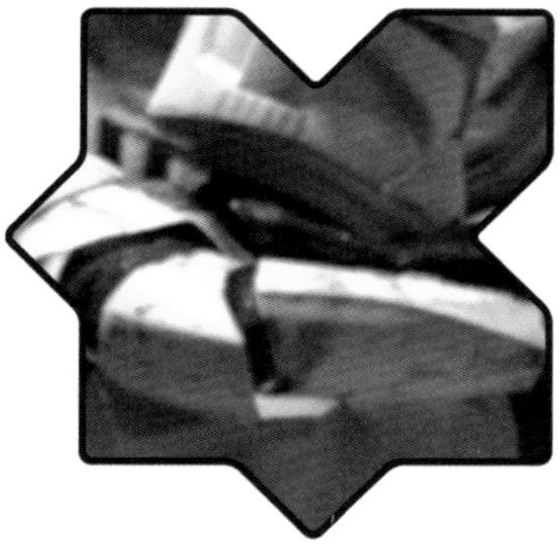

ENDOR

R2-D2

NABOO

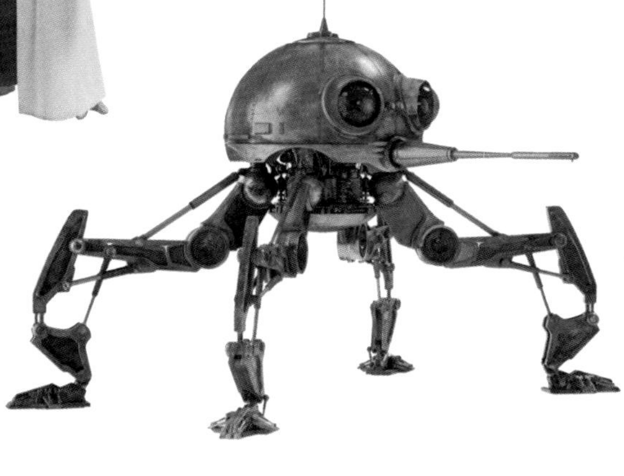